The Story of
Goldilocks

Illustrated by Suzy-Jane Tanner

It's fun to Read Along

Here's what you do-

These pictures are some of the characters and things the story tells about. Let the child to whom you are reading SEE and SAY them.

Then, as you read the story text and come to a picture instead of a word, pause and point to the picture for your listener to SEE and SAY.

You'll be amazed at how quickly children catch on and enjoy participating in the story telling.

ISBN 0-86163-813-1

Copyright © 1989 Award Publications Limited
This edition first published 1996
Second impression 1997

Published by Award Publications Limited,
27 Longford Street, London NW1 3DZ

Printed in Belgium

Baby
Bear

bears

beds

big
bed

big
bowl

big
chair

cushions

cottage

chairs

bowls

Daddy Bear

girl

medium bowl

small bowl

door

Goldilocks

medium chair

spoon

eyes

little chair

pieces

table

flowers

Mummy Bear

pillows

tears

forest

medium bed

stairs

small bed

GOLDILOCKS

Once upon a time there were three 🐻 who lived in a 🏠 deep in the 🌲 .

There was a great big and gruff 🐻 . There was a gentle middle-sized 🐻 and there was also a dear little 🐻 .

One fine morning 🐻 made some porridge for breakfast.

She poured it into three

different sized to cool. The three then set out for a walk in the .

While they were gone, a little knocked on their Her name was and she had been out gathering .

When nobody answered, she peeped inside the and saw three of porridge on the .

was very hungry. She tasted the steaming porridge in the 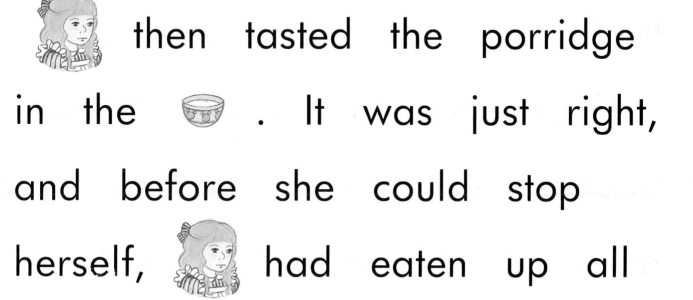. It was too hot.

She tasted the porridge in the . It was much too cold.

then tasted the porridge in the . It was just right, and before she could stop herself, had eaten up all the porridge in the .

saw three  in the room. There was a great for . There was a for and a for . sat down on the but it was much too hard. Then she sat on the , but that was far too soft.

When sat on the , it was not too hard, or too soft. She found it was just right.

But  was much too big and heavy for such a 🪑 . It broke into 🟫 .

🧒 picked herself up and then decided to go and see what was up 🪜 .

She found three  .

was now very sleepy, so she

tried to climb on to the

great which belonged to

. It was too high.

Next, lay down on the which belonged to  . It was very soft and she sank down much too low.

Yawning, climbed into the which belonged to . She found this was cosy and snug and felt just right. was soon fast asleep, so she did not hear the three  come back home.

 looked into his  .

"Somebody has been eating my porridge," he growled.

looked into her ,

with the 🥄 still resting in it.

"Somebody has been eating my porridge," she said in her middle-sized voice. When poor looked into his he found it was empty!

"Somebody has been eating my porridge," he cried in his squeaky little voice, "and it has all gone!"

 went to his .

"Somebody has been sitting in my ," he growled in his big deep voice.

"And somebody has been sitting in my ," said in her middle-sized voice. "The  are all untidy."

When looked for his all he could see were .

His little   filled with .

"Somebody has been sitting

in my  too," he sobbed, "and it's broken to ."

The three looked all over the room and under the but they could not find anyone. Then they went up to look in the bedrooms.

noticed that his were all creased and untidy.

"Somebody has been sleeping in my ," he called in his deep gruff voice.

 saw that her was rumpled. "Somebody has been sleeping in my 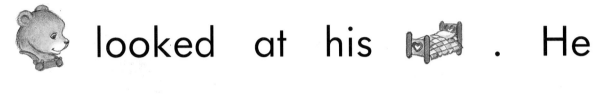," she said in her middle-sized voice.

 looked at his . He could hardly believe his own . "There is somebody still sleeping in my bed," he cried in his squeaky voice.

Just then opened her   and saw the three .

With a cry,  jumped out of the . She ran down the , out of the  and into the .

"Please stop!" called the . "We'll not harm you."

But  did not stop. She ran on through the  until she was safe in her own .  never went to visit the three  ever again.